GARFIELD

Wanetik?

JIM DAVIS

RR
RAVETTE PUBLISHING

First published by Ravette Publishing 2006.

_____

Printed and bound in Great Britain
for Ravette Publishing Limited,
Unit 3, Tristar Centre,
Star Road, Partridge Green,
West Sussex RH13 8RA

ISBN 10: 1-84161-264-2
ISBN 13: 978-1-84161-264-5

JIM DAVIS 10-12

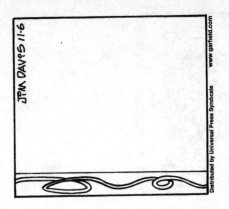

JIM DAVIS 11-27

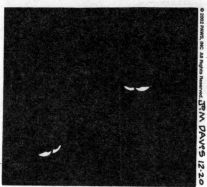

JIM DAVIS 12-26

OTHER GARFIELD BOOKS AVAILABLE

Pocket Books		Price	ISBN
Below Par		£3.50	1 84161 152 2
Compute This!		£3.50	1 84161 194 8
Don't Ask!		£3.99	1 84161 247 2
Double Trouble		£3.50	1 84161 008 9
Feed Me!		£3.99	1 84161 242 1
Get Serious	(new)	£3.99	1 84161 265 0
Gotcha!		£3.50	1 84161 226 X
I Am What I Am!		£3.99	1 84161 243 X
I Don't Do Perky		£3.50	1 84161 195 6
Kowabunga		£3.99	1 84161 246 4
Light Of My Life		£3.50	1 85304 353 2
Pop Star		£3.50	1 84161 151 4
S.W.A.L.K.		£3.50	1 84161 225 1

Theme Books	Price	ISBN
Behaving Badly	£4.50	1 85304 892 5
Cat Napping	£4.50	1 84161 087 9
Coffee Mornings	£4.50	1 84161 086 0
Creatures Great & Small	£3.99	1 85304 998 0
Entertains You	£4.50	1 84161 221 9
Healthy Living	£3.99	1 85304 972 7
Pigging Out	£4.50	1 85304 893 3
Slam Dunk!	£4.50	1 84161 222 7
Successful Living	£3.99	1 85304 973 5
The Seasons	£3.99	1 85304 999 9

2-in-1 Theme Books	Price	ISBN
All In Good Taste	£6.99	1 84161 209 X
Easy Does It	£6.99	1 84161 191 3
Lazy Daze	£6.99	1 84161 208 1
Licensed to Thrill	£6.99	1 84161 192 1
Out For The Couch	£6.99	1 84161 144 1
The Gruesome Twosome	£6.99	1 84161 143 3

Classics	Price	ISBN
Volume One	£6.99	1 85304 970 0
Volume Two	£5.99	1 85304 971 9
Volume Three	£5.99	1 85304 996 4
Volume Four	£6.99	1 85304 997 2
Volume Five	£5.99	1 84161 022 4
Volume Six	£6.99	1 84161 023 2
Volume Seven	£5.99	1 84161 088 7
Volume Eight	£5.99	1 84161 089 5
Volume Nine	£6.99	1 84161 149 2
Volume Ten	£6.99	1 84161 150 6
Volume Eleven	£6.99	1 84161 175 1
Volume Twelve	£6.99	1 84161 176 X

Classics (cont'd ...)		Price	ISBN
Volume Thirteen		£5.99	1 84161 206 5
Volume Fourteen		£6.99	1 84161 207 3
Volume Fifteen		£5.99	1 84161 232 4
Volume Sixteen		£5.99	1 84161 233 2
Volume Seventeen	(new)	£6.99	1 84161 250 2
Volume Eighteen	(new)	£6.99	1 84161 251 0

Little Books

C-c-c-caffeine		£2.50	1 84161 183 2
Food 'n' Fitness		£2.50	1 84161 145 X
Laughs		£2.50	1 84161 146 8
Love 'n' Stuff		£2.50	1 84161 147 6
Surf 'n' Sun		£2.50	1 84161 186 7
The Office		£2.50	1 84161 184 0
Zzzzzz		£2.50	1 84161 185 9

Miscellaneous

Garfield 25 years of me!		£7.99	1 84161 173 5
Treasury 7	(new)	£10.99	1 84161 248 0
Treasury 6		£10.99	1 84161 229 4
Treasury 5		£10.99	1 84161 198 0
Treasury 4		£10.99	1 84161 180 8
Treasury 3		£9.99	1 84161 142 5

All Garfield books are available at your local bookshop or from the publisher at the address below. Just tick the titles required and send the form with your payment to:-

RAVETTE PUBLISHING
Unit 3, Tristar Centre, Star Road, Partridge Green, West Sussex RH13 8RA

Prices and availability are subject to change without notice.

Please enclose a cheque or postal order made payable to **Ravette Publishing** to the value of the cover price of the book/s and allow the following for UK postage and packing:-

70p for the first book + 40p for each additional book
except Garfield Treasuries ... when please add £3.00 per copy for p&p.

Name ....

Address ....

....

....

....